WARPLANES OF THE
21ST CENTURY

WARPLANES OF THE 21ST CENTURY

Bill Yenne

Featuring the photography of
Erik Simonsen

BISON GROUP

First Published in 1990 by
Bison Books Ltd

Kimbolton House
117 A Fulham Rd
London SW3 6RL

ISBN 0 86124 665 9

Printed in Hong Kong

Designed by Bill Yenne

Edited by Joan Hayes

ACKNOWLEDGMENTS
The author wishes to thank David Kamiya of British Aerospace (Warton), Richard Stadler of Lockheed, E Ignaky of Messerschmitt-Bölkow-Blohm, Gail Rolka and Erik Simonsen.

All photos are by Erik Simonsen, with the following exceptions:
Aerospatiale 66 (both), 68 (bottom)
AMD-BA Aviaplans via Dassault Breguet 34
Boeing Helicopter 12, 12-13
British Aerospace 22, 23
Eurofighter Jagdflugzeug 26, 27
Lockheed Aeronautical Systems 18, 38 (both), 39, 40, 40-41, 42, 43,
    56-57, Gatefold (outside panels)
McDonnell Douglas 14, 56 (top)
Messerschmitt-Bölkow-Blohm 68 (top), 69, 70-71
NASA 52 (both)
NASDA 67 (both)
Northrop 60, 63, 64-65
Rockwell International 54, 55, 58 (both), 59
SAAB Scania 28, 28-29, 30, 31
Katsuhiko Tokunaga via Dassault Breguet 32, 33, 35
US Department of Defense 16 (bottom), 17 (bottom)

Page 1: **High above the fluffy cumulus cavorts a twenty-first century dart-shaped stealth fighter, its surface cloaked in a black, radar-absorbing protective coat.**
Pages 2-3: **France's Dassault Breguet Rafale (Hailstorm) flew at supersonic speeds during its first flight in 1986. Seen here in its combat colors, the Rafale D will be the backbone of French air power in the twenty-first century.**
Left: **This highly maneuverable Navy fighter, loaded for bear with wingtip-mounted AIM-9L Sidewinder air-to-air missiles, is based directly upon the Grumman X-29 research aircraft, which first flew in 1984.**

TABLE OF CONTENTS

INTRODUCTION
THINGS TO COME

Above: **The Testor F-19, which first appeared in 1986, was a projection of the possible appearance of the Lockheed stealth fighter whose designation was thought to be F-19, but which was actually F-117. The real F-19 is probably closer in appearance to Testor's airframe than to that of the F-117.**
Facing page: **This twenty-first century warplane traces its family tree back to Rockwell International's remotely piloted HIMAT demonstrator aircraft.**

In the William Cameron Menzies film **Things to Come**, a 1936 adaptation of the HG Wells classic which starred Raymond Massey and Cedric Hardwicke, the horrors of the Second World War were predicted with startling accuracy, as were the postwar boom in technological development, replete with giant flying wing warplanes which appear almost as hybrids of aircraft types—such as the B-35, B-49 **and B-2**—that actually **did** come.

Lacking Mr Wells' uncanny ability, or Mr Menzies' interpretive powers, it is often difficult to intuit the intricate turns the future will take because so many unforeseen events can alter the course of history. With aviation technology, the forecasters of the 1955-1965 era envisioned a continuation of the postwar aerospace boom and predicted routine, hypersonic, commercial flights and the presence of humans on Mars by 1980. Prophets of the world of aerospace have become more conservative of late, but it is still axiomatic that it always takes longer to bring a program on line than its original devotees optimistically project in its early phases.

In predicting the nature of military aerospace technology in the twenty-first century, we only can see so far as the first two decades, an era when the skyways will be dominated by the craft which make their maiden flights in the 1985-1999 time frame. Many of these aircraft will be in service in 2025, a fair number will still be around in 2050, and it is safe to say that most will influence the course of aerospace technology for much of the twenty-first century.

The warplanes that will spearhead the world's air forces in the twenty-first century began to take form in the late 1980s as aircraft, such as the F-14, F-15, F-16, Viggen and Tornado, matured and aerospace engineers began to draw lessons from them that could be applied to the fifth generation of jet warplanes since World War II. New materials were evaluated that could enhance both airframes and engines. Advanced development took place in metal-matrix, carbon fiber and ceramic composites for structural components, all of which had debuted in a big way in the 1970s.

In the generation of warplanes that came of age in the 1980s, nonmetal composites generally accounted for no more than a quarter of a typical aircraft's structure, compared to that which was comprised of conventional metals. In the warplanes on the drawing boards in the late

Above: **A US Air Force stealth fighter banks starboard as the first rays of the morning sun break across the clouds. For the first five years after they became operational, the Air Force's original stealth fighter—the Lockheed F-117—was like Bela Lugosi. It operated only at night.**

1980s, however, composites were being called upon to contribute half of an aircraft's structure. Today, the European Fighter Aircraft (EFA) consortium in Europe and Boeing in the United States are working on fighter concepts that will be composed of 60 percent fiber-reinforced composites.

Simultaneously, rapid progress was being made, both in Europe and the United States, in the development of improved avionics driven by very high speed integrated circuits (VHSIC) and operated on easily read, full-color, liquid crystal displays on the control panel, as well helmet-mounted displays, that were successors to the head-up displays (HUD) introduced in the 1970s. Eventually, HUD will be completely superseded by such helmet-mounted display systems, which will begin to go into service in the United States and Europe by the last half of the 1990s.

Advanced Fighter Technology Integration (AFTI) promises aircraft which will be voice controlled. In the US Air Force Project Forecast 2, completed in 1986, a study was undertaken to examine both developing and potential avionics. These studies were then integrated into a single, coordinated program called Super Cockpit, whose objective was to design the cockpit for the twenty-first century warplane. This Super Cockpit will contain not only voice-activated controls but head and eyesight-activated controls as well.

The first aircraft designed specifically to employ the secret 'stealth' technology for avoiding radar detection were unveiled in the late 1980s, but stealth characteristics are now considered so important that virtually no future combat aircraft would be considered front-line **without** stealth technology. This technology includes both the use of new radar-absorbing materials for the structure and surface of the aircraft, as well as a whole new approach to the overall shape of the airframe. The unorthodox appearance of both the F-117 and B-2 are harbingers of things to come.

Also coming will be air-to-air and air-to-ground missiles that will be

modified with clipped or folding fins, in addition to smokeless rocket motors to make them more 'stealthy.'

In the waning years of the twentieth century, aerospace engineers are focusing on areas of technology which would have been considered science fiction just a few years ago, but which are absolutely essential to the warplanes of the twenty-first century. These not only include the Super Cockpit and stealth technologies, but go beyond. Knowledge-based systems with artificial intelligence, which use human-like logic to operate avionics and weapons, are under study. So-called 'smart skin' or 'intelligent surface' materials are being developed to replace antennas, pods and domes that protrude from aircraft surfaces and increase radar vulnerability.

Nonlinear optics will use light in radically different ways for automatic tracking or to obviate atmospheric interference. Photonics technology not only increases the capacity of computers but helps to protect them from the scourges of electronic warfare. New lubricants are being introduced, as are new propellants. Among the latter are chemical propellants of increased power and decreased weight. Forward looking infrared sensors, that allow pilots to see through fog, rain and the dark of night, will become standard. Escape systems will also be faster and more reliable.

The evolution of aircraft systems has gone hand in glove with the evolution of tactics. When it was proven in the 1960s that surface-to-air missiles (SAMs) could shoot down high flying aircraft, tactics changed. Aircraft started flying closer to the ground, and systems were developed

Above: **A US Marine Corps Short Take-off and Landing (STOL) fighter bomber armed with AIM-9L Sidewinder air-to-air missiles on its wingtips and AGM-65 Maverick air-to-ground missiles underwing. The Marines consider air support of ground troops to be the essential mission of Marine airpower, so STOL characteristics are vital and an all-important consideration in the twenty-first century.**

Above: **This delta-shaped remotely piloted stealth aircraft could be airdropped by larger aircraft and sent on either attack or recon-naissance missions against heavily defend-ed enemy targets without fear for a crew-man's life.**

Opposite page: **As twilight falls, a US Air Force second generation spaceplane glides into Earth's atmosphere, bringing home its crew from a secret orbital reconnaissance mission.**

Similar in size to the never-flown Boeing X-20 of the 1960s, this advanced craft pro-vides the Air Force with a convenient means of accessing space routinely and inexpen-sively. Fifty years after it originally began using the word, the US Air Force will finally become a true 'aerospace' force in the twenty-first century.

to make it possible for aircraft—and cruise missiles as well—to fly literally at tree-top level. This eventually led to stealth technology, as aircraft designers sought to entirely eliminate the threat of being seen on radar.

In the 1950s and 1960s the key things that were sought in a high performance warplane were speed and altitude. It was assumed at that time that the warplanes of the future would be faster and higher flying. However, the wars in Vietnam and the Middle East between 1965 and 1975 taught us some important lessons about the realities of modern warfare. Today, designers are stressing a warplane's ability to take off and land in short distances, maneuver with ease in aerial combat and evade enemy radar. The X-29 and X-31 projects, for instance, are indicative of programs that are almost totally dedicated to exploring the limits of maneuverability.

Behind the technology, of course, are the costs of its development. In the 1970s and 1980s soaring costs resulted in the emergence of international consortiums that shared both the costs and results. A good example is Panavia, the Anglo-Italian-German group that developed the Tornado in the 1970s. In the twenty-first century such arrangements will be the rule rather than the exception, as the 1992 unification of European markets becomes a practical, rather than theoretical, reality.

In the United States, groups of aerospace firms have already been formed to develop the ATF and ATA projects, and in Europe a multina-tional consortium will build the European Fighter Aircraft (EFA). Trans-atlantic cooperation will also become more common, following the pattern of the British Aerospace-McDonnell Douglas collaboration, which brought about the Harrier, and that of the Rockwell and Messerschmitt-Bolkow-Blohm effort that produced the X-31.

The twenty-first century will see the advent of the most versatile warplanes ever, and it will also witness the routine use of manned, non-combatant, reusable spaceplanes. The United States first flew a space-plane in 1981 and the Soviet Union followed with an unmanned test flight of their own vehicle in 1988. By the turn of the century, the Japanese are expected to have followed suit, as are the French, under the auspices of the European Space Agency. Meanwhile, both West Germany and the United States are studying horizontal take-off spacecraft. These will be the first true spaceplanes, insofar as they will not only land on runways like today's Space Shuttle, but also take off from runways.

Potentially, the use of such craft will mean that the promise of routine use of space, which was once predicted for the 1970s, will at last become a reality in the twenty-first century.

The aircraft and the spacecraft pictured and discussed in this book are real aircraft, or at least serious concepts that will evolve into the twenty-first century's first generation of military aircraft. Among these aircraft are those that will be household words at the turn of the century, and the aircraft that will father, or grandfather, the aircraft and spacecraft that will be considered legendary by mid-century. This, then, is a preview of the aircraft book of the twenty-first century, a portfolio of things to come.

THE BELL/BOEING V-22 OSPREY
United States

Based on an idea that dates back to the Vietnam War, the Osprey evolved out of the XV-15 project and made its first flight on 23 March 1989 at Arlington, Texas. The venture, undertaken jointly by Boeing Helicopter and Bell Helicopter Textron, was to build a practical aircraft that could take off vertically like a helicopter, fold its huge rotors down and then use them to fly like an airplane.

This concept seemed ideal for 'special operations' or commando raids where no runways were available and where a craft was needed that had greater lifting power and greater speed than a conventional transport helicopter. The V-22 could also be used to effect vertical take-offs and landings on virtually any type of ship. The US Marine Corps planned to buy 552, while the Air Force and Navy intended to procure 105 between them. However, the V-22 project was canceled by Defense Secretary Richard Cheney within a month of the first flight for budgetary reasons. Congress, however, kept the program alive by deciding to postpone a final cancellation decision until fiscal year 1991.

Nevertheless, the V-22, or aircraft like it, will certainly be part of the world of combat aircraft. If the V-22 itself doesn't eventually go into production, it will form the basis for another which **will**. The idea is too good. If Congress doesn't buy it from Bell/Boeing, someone, somewhere will do it, and planes like these will be a reality in the twenty-first century.

The Bell/Boeing V-22—seen here during tests at Arlington, Texas in 1989—represents the first production-ready aircraft to employ the characteristics of both an airplane and a helicopter. It is powered by Allison T406-AD-400 engines. The V-22 was the object of intense controversy during its first year because of its development cost and the Pentagon's desire to save money.

THE McDONNELL DOUGLAS C-17
United States

In the twenty-first century, the combat airlifters in service throughout the world's air forces will have to be capable not only of carrying the largest equipment, but of being able to operate from the roughest of landing fields. The first aircraft to set the standard for these characteristics is the McDonnell Douglas C-17, which McDonnell Douglas began developing for the US Air Force in 1981. Using technology proven on the earlier YC-15 transport, the C-17 will use an externally blown flap system to greatly reduce final approach and landing speeds for routine, short-field landings. With this powered lift system, the engine thrust is directed to double-slotted flaps to produce additional lifting force. The flaps will be

made of titanium, using new technology superplastic forming/diffusion-bonding techniques. The C-17 is designed to be operated by a cockpit crew of two and a single loadmaster. The reduced flight crew complement is made possible through the use of an advanced digital avionics system.

The C-17 combines airlift capability for outsize combat equipment that can now be carried only by the larger Lockheed C-5, and short-field performance now provided only by the Lockheed C-130. This means added airlift not only for direct delivery to austere forward bases, but also for high priority combat mobility within a theater of operations. Only 850 runways in the world can accommodate C-5s and C-141s, while the C-17 can utilize 19,000. In the cargo compartment, the C-17 can carry Army wheeled vehicles in two side-by-side rows, and jeeps can be carried in triple rows. The C-17 is the only aircraft that can airdrop outsize firepower such as the Army's new infantry fighting vehicle. Three of these armored vehicles comprise one deployment load for the C-17. Similarly, the US Army's newest main battle tank, the M-1, can be carried in conjunction with other vehicles.

Above: A McDonnell Douglas C-17 in flight.
Opposite page: A US Air Force Military Airlift Command C-17 disgorges a US Army M1 Abrahms main battle tank (center) and other mechanized hardware at a rugged remote location as a second C-17 takes off for another load.

THE ANTONOV An-225 MRIYA
Soviet Union

For almost a decade the Lockheed C-5 Galaxy and the Boeing 747 jetliner were far and away the largest aircraft in service anywhere in the world. The Soviet Antonov An-124, which first flew in 1982 and entered service in 1987, was based on the Lockheed C-5. Though slightly shorter, it had a seven percent greater wingspan. However, for all practical purposes, these three airplanes were the same size.

Unknown in the West until November, 1988, the An-124 had a big brother. When the An-225 Mriya (Dream) first flew on 21 December 1988, it did seem like a dream. The Mriya was 28 feet longer than the C-5, with a wingspan 50 feet greater than an An-124. The largest airplane ever flown, the Mriya was also the only airplane ever to have a gross weight over one million pounds.

The An-225 is in essence a scaled-up An-124, which uses the same, albeit lengthened, fuselage and the same wings, that are extended by being moved outward on an expanded wing root structure. Whereas the An-124 was powered by four turbofan engines, the An-225 has six Lotarev D-19s, which deliver an aggregate total of 309,900 pounds of thrust, compared to 206,600 pounds available for the An-124, or 172,000 for the C-5B.

The An-225 can accommodate 16 large freight containers internally and has attachment points for carrying external cargo that can be carried in immense, streamlined containers that have a greater internal volume than most transport aircraft have in their fuselages. The An-225 is also the designated transport for the Soviet space shuttle orbiter, which it carries externally.

Mriya is used to provide heavy equipment transport services in remote regions of the Soviet Union where all-weather roads do not exist. Though flown publicly in the colors of Aeroflot, the Soviet state airline, the An-225 is no doubt an important aircraft in the service of Soviet Military Transport Aviation (VTA).

Because it is a major breakthrough in terms of size and tonnage, the Mriya is the harbinger of yet larger transports that will introduce a whole new scale to airlifts in the twenty-first century.

Opposite above: The Antonov An-225 Mriya, seen here with the Soviet Kosmolyet orbiter *Buran* (Snowstorm). *Opposite bottom:* The An-225 takes off enroute to the 1989 Abottsford Air Show, after a brief and ironic refuelling stop at Elmendorf AFB, Alaska. *Above:* The An-225 is the largest aircraft in the world, a distinction it could well retain for many years in the twenty-first century.

THE LOCKHEED F-117 NIGHTHAWK
United States

Above: The first photo of the F-117, released on 10 November 1988, showed what is perhaps the YF-117 service test aircraft with a 55 degree sweep to its wings. Note also the four pitot tubes on the aircraft's leading edge.

Facing page: As night falls, an F-117 'Wobblin' Goblin' descends to a lower operational altitude. The first live combat mission flown by F-117s came on the night of 20 December 1989 during the United States invasion of Panama, when they were used to attack the airfield at Rio Hato. Ironically, the F-117 was selected for the accuracy of its weapons targeting radar, rather than for its 'stealth' characteristics. The desire to test the innovative bird in live combat conditions was also a factor in the decision to commit it to battle.

The wars in Vietnam and the Middle East between 1965 and 1975 demonstrated a profound need for fighters and attack aircraft with a low radar cross section that could avoid enemy radar, particularly the radar systems of surface-to-air missiles (SAMs). This need became a concrete US Air Force development project as early as 1976. By 1977 a prototype aircraft employing 'stealth,' or radar-invisible, technology had been flown. Development of the Lockheed F-117 began in December 1978, and it made its first flight in June 1981. The first group of an eventual 59 F-117s became operational with the 4450th Tactical Group in October 1983 and were assigned to the secret operations center managed by Nellis AFB in the Nevada desert near Tonapah.

It had been widely supposed that this secret aircraft bore the F-19 designation because the Defense Department skipped from F-18 to F-20

Above and opposite: **A Lockheed F-117 banks deftly above the cumulus on a daytime training mission. From 1983 until as late as April 1989, the 'Goblin,' like the ghouls and goblins of popular myth, flew only at night. This was not so much out of supernatural concerns, but rather to keep its appearance concealed from both Soviet spy satellites and the prying eyes of eager airfans.**

in designating nonsecret aircraft. The F-117 designation was used, however, because the aircraft was assigned to the Tonapah site, which operates a number of 'unusual' aircraft designated in pre-1962 'century series' designations (F-112 to F-116, etc).

In the meantime, Testor, the scale model manufacturer, had released in 1986 its impression of a radar transparent fighter, which it designated F-19. The configuration of the actual F-19 became even more mysterious when the F-117 designation was announced. Some people suggested that the Nighthawk had actually **been** designated F-19, but that the Air Force had changed it to confuse those who had predicted it to be F-19. In all probability, one F-19 **does** exist, and it is probably more similar to the Testor F-19 than the Lockheed F-117.

Built by Lockheed in Burbank, California, the F-117s were transported to Tonapah at night by C-5 transports for final assembly and training flights. These flights were also conducted at night for the first five years and resulted in two crashes—in July 1986 and October 1987—that were well publicized, although the Air Force refused comment on the aircraft type involved. Indeed, the Air Force didn't even acknowledge the existence of the F-117 until November 1988, when a single photograph was released. This view of the heretofore secret bird was exhibited because the Air Force had decided to fly the F-117 in the daytime, although it would be April 1989 before any of them would be seen and photographed in daylight. The original YF-117 pictured in the official photo had a 55 degree wing sweep, compared to 67 degrees apparent in the F-117A photographed in 1989.

The Nighthawk is a good deal more angular than the Testor F-19, and its shape assures that no right angles can be seen from the aft. Therein lies an important aspect of its stealth nature.

The F-117 is powered by a pair of General Electric F404 turbofans and is theoretically capable of supersonic speeds, although it is designed structurally for subsonic missions. It is highly maneuverable, and hence is inherently unstable, a fact which led to the adoption of the unofficial, but ubiquitous, nickname 'Wobblin' Goblin.'

Above: Soaring high above the clouds, EAP embarks on her maiden flight on 8 August 1986. Piloted by Dave Eagles, EAP was airborne for one hour and seven minutes. During the flight the aircraft carried out general handling maneuvers and Dutch rolls and accelerated to a maximum speed of 1.1 Mach at 30,000 feet.

THE BRITISH AEROSPACE EAP
United Kingdom

The Experimental Aircraft Program (EAP) originated at British Aerospace (BAe) in 1981 as a project to create the technology for Britain's twenty-first century fighter aircraft. EAP was originally seen as a successor to the highly successful Panavia Tornado, an aircraft in which British Aerospace had played an important role. As planned, the EAP would not only provide the basis for a future British warplane but the basis for international cooperative projects as well. In fact, both Aeritalia in Italy and Messerschmitt-Bolkow-Blohm (MBB) in West Germany, who were BAe's partners in the Panavia Tornado, were slated to contribute major wing and control surface components to the EAP demonstrator.

The EAP aircraft was designed to be powered by a pair of Turbo-Union RB.199 engines, similar to those used on the Tornado, which are also a product of Anglo-Italian-German cooperation. It has been suggested that the production versions of the EAP, if such were to be built, would be powered by the new Eurojet EJ-200 engines, which are being developed by an international group for use in the European Fighter Aircraft (EFA). As was the case with Turbo-Union, Britain's Rolls Royce is part of the Eurojet consortium.

The idea behind the Tornado, and originally behind the EAP, was that tri-national industry would develop and build the aircraft and the air forces of the three nations would buy them. In 1982, however, West Germany and Italy withdrew governmental support for the EAP. Aeritalia and MBB remained involved in the project and both contributed substantially to the EFA.

Above: **The EAP passes low overhead, showing to perfection the layout of the four British Aerospace Sky Flash missiles and two wingtip-mounted ASRAAMs.**

As a result, the EAP demonstrator, which rolled out at Warton, England on 16 April 1986, was not seen so much as a prototype of a specific aircraft, but rather as an amalgam of the technology that would be present in the RAF's fighter fleet—and possibly that of other air arms as well—at the turn of the century, and beyond.

The EAP demonstrator is designed to be capable of a high degree of maneuverability out of a high angle of attack at moderate speed. It is equipped with triple redundant fly-by-wire controls and a state-of-the-art cockpit, which truly displayed the environment in which a twenty-first century pilot would expect to find himself.

The EAP made its first flight on 8 August 1986, only one month before it was to become the center of attention at the Farnborough Air Show. Dave Eagles, executive director of flight operations at BAe's Warton facility, piloted the EAP on its debut flight, attaining a speed of Mach 1.1.

The EAP aircraft went on to fulfill an extensive test program, the results of which will provide the basic building blocks for the warplanes that will evolve from the joint efforts of British Aerospace and its future twenty-first century partners.

THE EUROJET EFA
United Kingdom, Italy, West Germany, et al

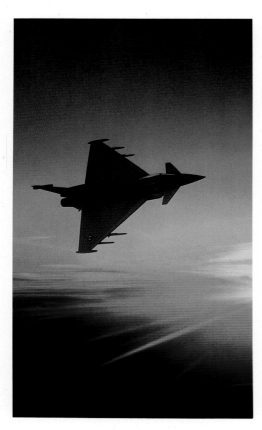

Above and opposite page: **The dawn of the twenty-first century will see the EFA head off on a top secret reconnaissance mission. EFA's high performance as a weapon system is achieved through the full integration of the flight control system with the other avionic and utility systems.**

The Eurojet Jagdflugzeug European Fighter Aircraft (EFA) evolved from the same roots as the British Aerospace EAP. The concept was the same: to build on the experience of the multinational Panavia Tornado project to construct what would amount to a new generation of aircraft designed for the same roles for which the Tornado had been designed more than a decade earlier.

After 1982, when West Germany and Italy ended their involvement in the cooperative venture which British Aerospace would go on to uni-laterally develop into the EAP, there was still a great deal of interest in Europe for a multinational fighter. This interest was not just in the original Panavia countries, but in the Netherlands, Spain and even France, where combat aircraft procurement tended to favor domestic builders to a more substantial degree than anywhere else on the continent. It was this kind of a potential consortium which United Kingdom Defence Minister Michael Heseltine described at the time as 'impossibly ambitious.'

When an agreement was finally reached in August 1985, it was again the Panavia partners alone who signed. West Germany and the United Kingdom each agreed to a 38 percent participation, with Italy underwriting the remaining 26 percent. When the production consortium was formed in June 1986, however, it included not only British Aerospace, Aeritalia and MBB, but Spain's CASA as well. In the meantime, United States Defense Secretary Caspar Weinberger had announced in December 1985 that his department would work with the consortium to develop a 'balanced mix of common subsystems' that would also be produced for use on the new American Advanced Tactical Fighter (ATF). The United States would not, however, buy EFA as its ATF because the Yanks needed something heavier and longer ranging than that which the Europeans had in mind.

Soon after the multinational Eurofighter Jagdflugzeug GmbH consortium was formed in June 1986, the participants began to define what the EFA would be like and what types of missions it would have to fulfill. They rejected the suggestion made by France that they adapt France's Dassault Breguet Rafale to meet the EFA requirement. Nevertheless, the full-scale mockup that was shown at the 1986 Farnborough Air Show in September looked a great deal like the Rafale and the British Aerospace EAP demonstrator, both of which were flown publicly for the first time at the show.

Ultimately, a great deal of what has been learned from the EAP program will be integrated into the British Aerospace contribution to the Eurofighter. Indeed, the EFA has the same delta plan form and canard control system as the EAP, and it has roughly the same dimensions and gross weight.

Above: **To give it the smooth grace to race through the clouds, the design of the EFA incorporates extensive use of carbon fiber composites, glass-reinforced plastics and new lightweight metal alloys.**

In September 1987 the Chiefs of Air Staffs of the four nations signed the European Staff Requirement for Development (ESR-D). The requirements of the current four EFA participating nations call for a total of about 800 production aircraft, with the production being equitably shared in relation to the number of units ordered by each country. The production of each major sub-assembly will be allocated as far as possible to a single nation. However, final assembly will take place in all four nations, and all of them will participate in the flight test program.

After two years of detailed project definition, full-scale development of the EFA commenced in the beginning of 1988 and will continue until 1999. Production began with eight prototypes (including two trainer versions), with the first flight scheduled in 1991. To speed the program and reduce risks, initial flight plans involved limited interim use of Turbo-Union RB.199 engines (as used in the Panavia Tornado) until the Eurojet EJ-200 engines become available. A total of more than 2000 hours will be flown by these prototypes before the delivery of the first production aircraft to the nations. Special attention has been directed towards achieving significant improvements in reliability, availability and operating costs. These aspects have been given the same priority as the achievement of performance parameters.

To meet European Staff Requirement the aircraft must be extremely

agile and capable of air combat maneuvers not possible in the previous generation of fighters. Special emphasis has therefore been placed on low wing loading, high thrust to weight ratio, excellent all around pilot vision and 'carefree handling.' A canard delta layout—similar to that which British Aerospace adopted for the EAP—together with the adaptive control system ensures high levels of both subsonic and supersonic performance. The aircraft's high performance is matched by the attack, identification and defense systems, which feature long range radar and air-to-air missiles.

Above: **Symbolizing the cooperation of the four countries involved in its development, the EFA bears a single insignia representing each country as part of a unified whole.**

This performance is provided against an expected in-service airframe life of 25 years. The latest computer aided design and manufacturing methods were employed in order to ensure that the objectives of the program were met.

EFA is seen by the Eurofighter consortium as the 'fighter aircraft of the future,' one designed to meet the requirements of four major North Atlantic Treaty Organization (NATO) air forces. It has been conceived as a versatile fighter and ground attack aircraft, with a very high performance, coupled with low costs of acquisition and ownership. Its reliability and ease of maintenance provide the high availability required in peace and war, filling not only the needs of the 1990s but those which will exist well into the twenty-first century.

THE SAAB-SCANIA JAS-39 GRIPEN
Sweden

The SAAB-Scania JAS-39 Gripen (Griffon) was conceived as the twenty-first century successor to the SAAB-Scania JA-37 Viggen (Thunderbolt), which entered service with the Swedish air force (**Flygvapnet**) in 1971. With the awesome firepower of the Warsaw Pact less than 30 minutes flying time from anywhere in Sweden, the Swedish defense establishment has always maintained a vigilant defense posture. Furthermore, in order to safeguard its neutrality, which it maintained even throughout World War II, Sweden has nurtured and developed an independent domestic arms industry. This has included the SAAB family of first-line combat aircraft, which went into production just after World War II, and has culminated at the end of the century with the Gripen.

Developed to perform in the fighter, attack and reconnaissance roles, the JAS-39 was rolled out at Linkoping, Sweden on 26 April 1987, SAAB's 50th birthday. The first flight, however, was delayed by avionics software development until 9 December 1988, when SAAB's chief test pilot, Stig Holmstrom, took the Gripen up to 21,000 feet at Mach .8 on the maiden flight.

The program suffered a serious setback when the first prototype was involved in a crash during its sixth flight on 2 February 1989. As the second prototype had not yet been completed, this left SAAB without a demonstrator, which was essential in lining up the export customers vital to the financial success of the program.

Potential export customers included Denmark and Finland, who had both bought earlier SAAB fighter aircraft, and who are natural customers because they share the terrain and weather conditions for which SAAB

Far left: Test pilot Stig Holmstrom brings home the JAS-39 Gripen after its successful first flight on 9 December 1988. *Above:* JAS—a Swedish abbreviation for Fighter, Attack and Reconnaissance—lives up to its name. Each JAS-39 aircraft will be capable of performing all three missions.

Above: **The Gripen's powerful pulse-doppler radar with dedicated functions for each type of mission contributes significantly to the aircraft's combat efficiency.** ***Opposite page:*** **The JAS-39 in vertical flight.**

optimized its warplanes. Because of the rugged Scandinavian topography and the possibility that conventional airfields would be destroyed early in a potential conflict, the Gripen is designed for high reliability and simple maintenance. In the field, conscript technicians can quickly prepare the aircraft for the next flight. The Gripen has an Auxiliary Power Unit and a comprehensive, built-in test system. It also offers the possibility of a new basing concept which uses dispersed road bases or small airfields.

The combat scenarios of the twenty-first century will be characterized by extensive electronic warfare and concentrated attacks on airfields and communications centers, so the Gripen has been designed to survive with full operational capability under such conditions. As well as being difficult to detect on the ground and in the air due to low signatures, the aircraft also has comprehensive countermeasures equipment and a high ability to operate in a combat environment.

Flight characteristics and performance on the Gripen are dimensioned for fighter missions with high demands on speed, acceleration and maneuverability. The combination of delta wing and all moving canard gives it excellent take-off, flight performance and landing characteristics.

The flight characteristics of the Gripen are achieved through a fly-by-wire control system with built-in redundancy. This gives the aircraft outstanding maneuverability and safety, as well as enabling it to carry a wide variation in payload. The JAS-39 weighs only half as much as its forerunner, the JA-37 Viggen, but can carry the same weapons load. This has been accomplished through developments in materials, avionics and engine technology.

Delivery of the first production series of 30 Gripens to the Swedish air force will begin in the mid-1990s. The total requirement, as estimated by the supreme commander of the Swedish armed forces, will be 21 to 23 squadrons, or 350 to 400 aircraft.

THE DASSAULT BREGUET RAFALE
France

Conceived as a replacement for the Mirage 2000, which entered service in 1983, the Rafale (Hailstorm) is seen as the backbone of the French air force (**Armée de l'Air**) in the years **after** 2000. France would also like to see the Rafale as an export product and, indeed, Dassault Breguet, France's premier warplane builder for nearly four decades, has a customer base in as many as 26 countries. Dassault Breguet has in fact proposed the Rafale to NATO nations as a successor to the General Dynamics F-16 or as an alternative to the Eurofighter EFA, and Saudi Arabia has expressed a great deal of interest. France itself is tentatively planning for 250 Rafales for its air force and 85 for its navy.

The Rafale is a fast, lightweight fighter with a high degree of maneuverability achieved through the use of canard control surfaces similar to those of the British Aerospace EAP, which was developed simultaneously

Below: **Heading skyward, a test pilot readies the Rafale A for another series of complex maneuvers. The aircraft will act as a full-size flying test bed for trying out the technical options for the future tactical combat aircraft (ACT) and the Marine aircraft (ACM).** *Opposite page:* **The operational efficiency of the Rafale D is enhanced by the integration of advanced air-to-air and air-to-ground communications systems.**

in the United Kingdom. Like all of the latest generation jet fighters, it incorporates digital fly-by-wire avionics and is constructed with a high percentage of carbon fiber composite material. Armament centers on a 30mm DEFA-554 cannon and wingtip mounted Matra Magic air-to-air missiles.

Built at St Cloud, the Rafale A prototype was shipped to Dassault Breguet's test field at Istres in December 1985, from which it made its first flight on 4 July 1986. Guy Mitaux-Maurouard, Dassault Breguet's chief test pilot, took the Rafale up to Mach 1.3 and 36,000 feet on this first flight. Rafale A was powered by a General Electric F404 turbofan engine, but the production Rafale Ds will all be equipped with French-built SNECMA M88 turbofans.

Approval for development of the production series Rafale D came in April 1988, and in October 1988, after test operations from the carrier **Foch**, the French navy decided to go ahead with its development of a carrier-based Rafale M (Marine) to replace the Vought F-8Es then in service.

By the twenty-first century, the Rafale will be the standard tactical aircraft of France and perhaps of the air forces of many other European countries.

Below: **By May of 1989, the Rafale A had logged 400 flights and attained a maximum speed of Mach 2.** *Opposite page:* **Turnaround between missions for the Rafale D will be exceptionally fast, with refuelling requiring only four to seven minutes, depending on the configuration.**

THE MITSUBISHI FS-X
Japan

Since it began to rebuild the air arm of its self defense force in the 1950s, Japan has relied principally on American designed aircraft, such as the F-86, F-4 and F-15, although many of them have been built in Japan under license from American companies. The only major tactical aircraft designed in Japan since World War II was the Mitsubishi F-1, a ground attack aircraft that had been in service for two decades when the Japanese government started looking for a replacement in 1985. Japan looked at the Panavia Tornado, the General Dynamics F-16 and the McDonnell Douglas F/A-18, but Japanese industry urged the government to consider a domestically produced aircraft instead.

In October 1987, Defense Minister Yuko Kurihara and US Secretary of Defense Caspar Weinberger reached an agreement under which Mitsubishi would develop a Fighter Strike, Experimental (FS-X) aircraft for the Japanese Air Self Defense Force (JASDF), which would be based on the General Dynamics F-16, but **built** in Japan. This agreement was opposed in the United States on the grounds that it would involve the transfer of American technology to Japan. Such opposition failed to take into account that Mitsubishi was **already** building F-15s and that the F-16 technology was more than a decade old.

The FS-X will eventually evolve into standard equipment with the JASDF by the turn of the century, with nearly 100 in service by that time.

Below and opposite: **Mitsubishi's FS-X for the Japanese Air Self Defense Force looks very much like an F-16 from the wing-tip mounted AIM-9 Sidewinders to the one-piece, horizontal tail surfaces, but it is largely a new airplane incorporating such features as the canards. Nevertheless, General Dynamics will build as much as 40 percent of the FS-X.**

THE LOCKHEED/BOEING/ GENERAL DYNAMICS F-22 and THE NORTHROP/ McDONNELL DOUGLAS F-23

United States

Above: **Early Lockheed ATF concepts dating from 1984 (top) and 1986 (bottom).** *Facing page:* **A pair of Lockheed F-22s maneuver among the cloud tops.**

By the middle of the 1980s, the US Air Force was seriously beginning to consider a successor to the McDonnell Douglas F-15 Eagle, which had been its top air superiority fighter for more than ten years. This aircraft was known generically as the Advanced Tactical Fighter (ATF) until preliminary proposals were submitted in July 1986 and the F-22 and F-23 designations were assigned. Initial proposals were submitted by Boeing, General Dynamics, Grumman, Lockheed, McDonnell Douglas, Northrop and Rockwell International. The Air Force announced that it would select two contractor proposals and buy two aircraft from each. These aircraft, YF-22A and YF-23A, would be flown in competition with each in the early 1990s and the winner would go into production, with a total of 750 aircraft to be purchased through 2006.

By November 1986 the proposals had been evaluated and Northrop and Lockheed were given parallel $691 million development contracts. The selection seemed to underscore the importance of stealth technology in the ATF program because both of these companies were well into their respective B-2 and F-117 stealth programs at that time. These two contractors in turn teamed up with other 'contestants' to form development teams, with only Grumman and Rockwell not being involved in the ATF work. In the case of the YF-22A, for example, Lockheed would build the forward fuselage and be responsible for the stealth aspects of overall design; Boeing would build the wings, aft fuselage and offensive avionics; and General Dynamics would complete the control surfaces and defensive avionics.

The centerpiece of the avionics in both ATF contenders' proposals was the Integrated Electronic Warfare System (INEWS). The aircraft themselves will take advantage of the best of the quickly evolving world of fighter aircraft technology to deliver maximum agility, short airfield compatibility and the capability of top speeds above the Mach 1.5 threshold.

Unlike older counterparts in Europe, such as the Rafale, Gripen or Eurofighter, export marketing is not an important aspect of the ATF's future. However, the US Congress decreed in July 1988 that the US Navy, as well as the US Air Force, should participate in the ATF program.

Because of the escalating costs of new high technology fighters, Congress intended that whichever aircraft—YF-22A or YF-23A—won the ATF award, it should be able to serve the Navy's needs as well as those of the Air Force. In July 1989, however, it became clear that the naval ATF (NATF) wouldn't be ready for squadron service until the year 2000, so the Navy indicated that it would rather go ahead with the Grumman F-14D, which would be available much sooner.

The Navy also recalled the TFX program from the 1960s, which was an earlier, failed attempt to develop an advanced tactical fighter that could serve the needs of both the Air Force and Navy. If the NATF were developed, however, it would add as many as 600 units to the 750 aircraft that the Air Force expects to buy.

The ATF plans call for greatly improved reliability and maintainability with high sortie generation rates. The design goal for all areas is twice as good as the F-15 weapon system. The ATF plans also call for an increased survivability rate through a first-look, first-kill opportunity by

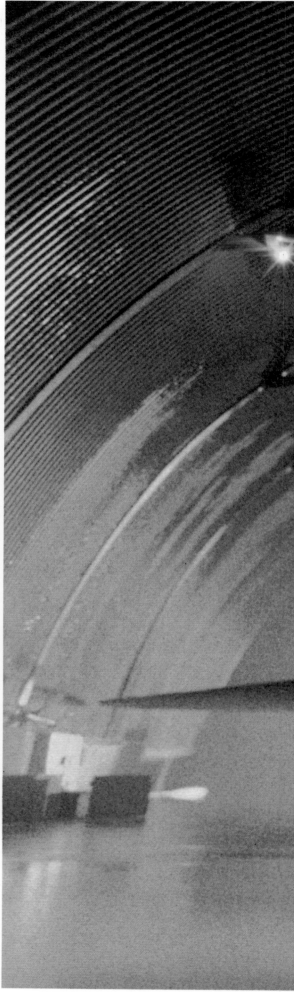

Above: Advanced flight station technologies pictured in this 1988 artist's concept by Eric Van Der Palen represent many being developed by Lockheed Aeronautical Systems Company for integration into its design for the Lockheed YF-22 Advanced Tactical Fighter (ATF).

The programmable nature of the displays eliminates the need for dedicated gauges and increases the amount of display space needed because of increased information coming in from the aircraft's more sophisticated sensors. A specially articulated pilot's seat automatically compensates for the increased and sustained gravitational forces the ATF pilot will experience in flight.

At right: Like a mysterious, mythical beast, a Lockheed F-22 crouches in its misty lair.

Above and opposite: **On the cusp of nightfall, a pair of US Air Force F-22s smoke the bandits in a twisting, turning dogfight over a twenty-first century battlefield. Maneuverability and close-in dogfighting ability will be as important to fighters of 2017 as they were to the fighters of 1917.**

the use of reduced observables and passive sensors. To decrease the reaction time to enemy threats, increased supersonic cruise and maneuverability goals have been set. To improve operations from battle-damaged runways, the ATF will significantly reduce the take-off and landing distances of that of today's front-line fighters. A greatly increased combat radius, using internal fuel, will allow ATF pilots the upper hand in air superiority.

Extensive use of VHSIC (Very High Speed Integrated Circuits), common modules and high speed databases will be used. The avionics suite will be a highly integrated system which maximizes performance while it minimizes the pilot's workload. Other technologies being evaluated include voice command-control, shared antennas, Ada software, expert systems, advance data fusion/cockpit display, INEWS, Integrated Communications, Navigation, Identification Avionics (ICNIA) and fiber optics data transmission. Weapons will include advanced versions of both the AIM-9 and AIM-120 air-to-air missiles.

By the time the ATF begins to enter the force, it will have been more than two decades since the introduction of the F-15. The ATF is the American air superiority fighter of the twenty-first century. It will be designed to be both lethal and survivable while penetrating high threat airspace. This will be achieved through a proper balance of increased speed and range, enhanced defensive avionics, reduced observables and an emphasis on reliability and maintainability.

THE GENERAL DYNAMICS/ McDONNELL DOUGLAS A-12

United States

In the mid-1980s, as the US Air Force was starting to define its twenty-first century fighter requirements under the ATF program, the US Navy's Naval Air Systems Command (Navair) was doing the same with its need for a new generation, all-weather attack aircraft. Unlike the ATF program, however, which was widely discussed in the news media, the Navy's Advanced Tactical Aircraft (ATA) project was kept secret until 1986 because of its stealth nature, and even then Navair revealed as little data as it could. For example, the Navair phone directory listed Captain Sam Sayers as ATA program coordinator but didn't list an address!

In November 1986, two teams—Grumman/Northrop and McDonnell Douglas/General Dynamics—were selected to participate in the demonstration and evaluation phase of the ATA project. In October 1987 the latter team was chosen to build the aircraft, which was designated A-12 in 1988.

In July 1988 the US Congress insisted that the Air Force and Navy cooperate on both the Air Force's ATF **and** the Navy's ATA programs in order to save money. Air Force Secretary Russell Rourke had said in March 1986 that the ATA **could** be used as an eventual replacement for the Air Force's F-111, so there was room for shared development. This could amount to 450 Navy A-12s and as many as 550 for the Air Force.

The most interesting publicly known controversy surrounding the A-12 involved the choice of a name. Most names that were proposed alluded to the stealth nature of the airplane, as it would be the first aircraft, after the F-117 and B-2, in which stealth characteristics are paramount. Included among the intriguing list of choices were Avenger 2, Masked Avenger, Enforcer, Ghost, Mystic, Seabat, Shadow, Stingray and Veil. When chosen, the name Avenger constituted an allusion to the Grumman TBF Avenger, one of the Navy's most important attack aircraft of the World War II era. It was also the plane flown by LTJG (later President of the United States) George Bush.

The choice of the name Avenger was somewhat awkward, however, because Grumman lost the ATA competition, and the aircraft that the A-12 replaces is the Grumman A-6.

Facing page: **Clad in its severe 'iceberg' camouflage, this A-12 concept by Erik Simonsen displays wing surfaces reminiscent of the Douglas F4D Skyray of the 1950s. Who would have realized then that the Skyray's wings were stealthy? Inside the A-12, the cockpit features, among other advancements, 8 x 8-inch, touch-sensitive, liquid crystal displays.**

THE MIKOYAN GUREVICH MiG-29
Soviet Union

Since the dawn of the age of jet fighters, the 'MiGs' of the Soviet design bureau Mikoyan Gurevich have always played an important role in the balance of worldwide power. The MiG-15 was a potent adversary to United Nations forces in Korea, and the Mach 3 MiG-25 vied with the Lockheed YF-12 as the fastest warplane ever built.

The MiG-29 (NATO codename 'Fulcrum'), which entered service with the Soviet air force in 1985, represents a new generation in Soviet warplanes. The MiG-29 was first flown in 1979, but was not seen in the West until a tightly guarded appearance at Rissala AB in Finland in 1986. However, in 1988 and 1989 the Soviets displayed the aircraft in an unprecedented and open manner at the International Air Shows in Farnborough, Paris and Abottsford, Canada.

Similar in size, weight and configuration to the McDonnell Douglas F/A-18 Hornet, the MiG-29 is powered by a pair of Isotov RD-33 turbofan engines, delivering a better than even thrust to weight ratio. The MiG-29

Below: **A Mikoyan Gurevich MiG-29UB trainer makes an appearance at the 1989 Paris Air Show.** *Opposite:* **A MiG-29 taking off at dusk for a night mission for which it is aptly configured with all-weather avionics.**

Above and opposite: **During its appearances at Paris and Abottsford in 1989, this Soviet Air Force MiG-29 thrilled the audiences with steep takeoffs and thunderous landings. Considered the leading edge of Soviet warplane technology at the time, the MiG-29 will be the backbone of Soviet tactical air power in the early twenty-first century.**

is also more maneuverable than earlier Soviet fighters, a factor which made the aerobatics that it displayed at Farnborough and Paris very impressive. Indeed, Mikoyan chief test pilot Anatoly Kvotchur performed 'tail slide' maneuvers with the aircraft in which he pointed the nose straight up, pulled the throttles back and stopped the big jet fighter briefly in mid-air, whereupon its tail began to slide down before the engine was throttled up again. A thrilling maneuver, the 'tail slide' is often performed by piston-engined aircraft, but rarely by jets, especially high performance fighters.

The agile Fulcrum represents the Mikoyan Bureau's first operational aircraft to be constructed through the extensive use of carbon composites, and as such, the finished surfaces are not as clear as those on comparable Western jets. It is also the first Soviet fighter with a form of 'look down/shoot down' radar, a system that compensates for 'ground clutter' when a pilot targets low-flying enemy aircraft. Unlike its contemporaries in the West, however, the MiG-29 has hydraulically actuated, rather than digital, fly-by-wire technology.

The MiG-29 has been put into service in East Germany, India, Iraq, North Korea, Syria and Yugoslavia, as well in the the Soviet Union, and it promises to serve as the backbone of Soviet and Eastern Bloc tactical forces in the early years of the twenty-first century.

THE SUKHOI Su-27
Soviet Union

In the 1970s the Sukhoi Design Bureau emerged as a major producer of Soviet fighters, second only to Mikoyan Gurevich. The Su-27 (NATO codename 'Flanker'), which entered service in 1986, is intended to serve as the Soviet Union's first-line air superiority fighter in the 1990s and beyond the turn of the century.

It is similar in configuration, size and purpose to the American McDonnell Douglas F-15, and shares a great many innovative features with its notable contemporary, the MiG-29. Among these characteristics are carbon composite structural components, improved 'look down/ shoot down' radar, a high degree of maneuverability and a thrust to weight ratio which represents a great improvement over earlier generation Soviet fighters. Powered by two 27,500 lb thrust Lyulka AL-31F turbofan engines, the Su-27 holds several important time-to-height records, including a climb to 39,370 feet in 55.5 seconds.

In operational service with the Soviet Air Force, the Su-27 is used both as an escort for the Sukhoi Su-24 (Fencer) long range fighter-bomber and as an air defense interceptor. In the latter role, its look down/shoot down radar would permit the Su-27 to attack low-flying cruise missiles, which are designed to use the 'ground clutter' of hills, valleys and other terrain features to 'hide' in.

Above and opposite: The Sukhoi Su-27 was designed as an interceptor for the job of patrolling the vast reaches of Soviet airspace. The wingtip rails are fitted with AA-10 (NATO code name Alamo) air-to-air missiles for operational intercept missions. Like the MIG-29, the Su-27 was displayed at the 1989 Paris Air Show.

THE GRUMMAN X-29
United States

Conventional swept wings were first adopted in the 1940s, having been determined to be the optimal configuration for jet aircraft flying at speeds of Mach .7 or greater. The idea of **forward** swept wings evolved at the same time, and indeed the German Junkers Ju-287 jet bomber was flown with forward swept wings in 1944.

Theoretically, forward swept wings provide more maneuverability at slower speeds than conventionally swept wings. However, the advantages seemed to be greatly outweighed by the problem of controllability. For this reason, forward swept wings were used on smaller aircraft such as the postwar German Hansa Jet, but not seriously considered for high performance military aircraft until the 1970s, when high speed computers and digital fly-by-wire controls obviated the drawbacks.

Sponsored by the US Defense Advance Research Projects Agency (DARPA), the X-29 program began in 1977, with Grumman being selected as the primary contractor in 1981. Two prototypes were built, the

first being completed in 1984 and delivered to Edwards AFB for its first flight on 14 December 1984, with Grumman test pilot Chuck Sewell at the controls. The X-29 proved to be so maneuverable that Sewell conducted a series of unauthorized barrel rolls on his third flight without any loss of controllability.

Subsequently, the first X-29 was flown for 242 flights, more than any of the other X-series aircraft, including the famous X-15, of which three individual aircraft made 199 flights between 1959 and 1968. During the course of these flights, test pilots from the US Air Force, US Navy and NASA took turns at the controls, evaluating forward sweep technology, not only as a research project, but also from the standpoint of operational applications. The second X-29 arrived at Edwards AFB shortly before the first X-29 was permanently retired, and made its first flight on 23 May 1989. The test flight program, which took the X-29 to speeds of up to Mach 1.8, focused principally on maneuverability, especially high angle of attack maneuvering.

In the twenty-first century, the forward swept wing technology evaluated by the X-29 in the 1980s and 1990s will be commonplace, as designers strive for the high degree of maneuverability that such a configuration permits.

Opposite, below: The X-29A Forward Swept Wing is rolled out at Grumman Aircraft Corporation on 27 August 1984. *Opposite, above:* The X-29 takes to the skies for a successful second flight on 4 February 1985. *Above:* This twenty-first century fighter is clearly derived from the X-29 configuration.

THE X-30 NATIONAL AEROSPACE PLANE
United States

Below and opposite: **These 1988 views of Rockwell International's NASP show a simple delta wing and a fuselage swelled to contain not only a payload area, but liquid hydrogen fuel as well. The cockpit affords no direct forward view for the pilot, so landings would have to be accomplished via a closed circuit video system.**

The inclusion of the moon (*at right*) is only decorative, as flights to lunar orbit are not intended for the NASP, nor indeed are they practical for any *winged* spacecraft. On the other hand, Rockwell built Apollo, the only manned craft ever to orbit the moon, so anything is *possible*.

The notion of a hypersonic 'single-stage-to-orbit' spaceplane has been on drawing boards around the world for nearly half a century, but the enormous costs and technical problems inherent in such a project have served to **keep** it on the drawing boards.

The project specifically designated X-30 began in 1986 when NASA and the Department of Defense issued $450 million worth of development contracts to Boeing, General Dynamics, Lockheed, McDonnell Douglas and Rockwell International. The scope of the project had been defined by President Ronald Reagan in his February 1986 State of the Union address, when he referred to the commercial potential of a National Aerospace Plane (NASP) that could be flown from the United States to Tokyo in only a few hours. The commercial NASP which Reagan described in his speech as the **Orient Express** was not the X-30, however, but rather a second generation NASP, part of a **family** of single-stage-to-orbit spaceplanes which will become common sights in the twenty-first century.

The X-30 is also distinct from the NASA High Speed Civil Transport (HSCT) being developed by Boeing and McDonnell Douglas for service as early as the first decade of the twenty-first century. In fact, since 1987

the Defense Department (specifically Air Force Systems Command) role in the X-30 project has evolved to a much higher degree than the NASA civilian role. All artist conceptions that were originally released showing the X-30 in jolly 'Air Force One' type markings were recalled in April 1987 at the behest of Congress, as the program became more of a secret military project.

The original timeline adopted for the X-30 called for the first atmospheric flight test to be conducted in 1993, and this projection held true until July 1988, when President George Bush's White House National Space Council agreed to a first flight postponement to 1997 or beyond. The thinking surrounding the project had by this time progressed to wanting to keep NASP a 'research project' rather than a 'prototype development effort.'

Unless the delay means that the X-30 is preceded into space by a German or Soviet spaceplane, it will be the first craft capable of taking off from a runway, traveling into space and then landing on a runway at the end of its flight. The X-30, of which a probable two will be built, will be approximately 150 feet long with a weight of 30,000 pounds, not including about 100,000 pounds of fuel. The fuel being suggested is 'slush,' or partially frozen, hydrogen, which is 16 percent more dense than liquid hydrogen and would offer a 30 percent savings in overall size and weight of the X-30. Scramjet (Supersonic Combustion ramjet) engines have also been proposed, but they are only practical between speeds of Mach 1 and Mach 6, and the X-30 will be operated between subsonic speeds and atmospheric re-entry speeds of Mach 25.

In the twenty-first century single-stage-to-orbit spaceplanes will provide easy and convenient access to space for a wide variety of applications, ranging from those now undertaken by the Space Shuttle to missions that have yet to be imagined.

THE ROCKWELL/ MBB X-31
United States/West Germany

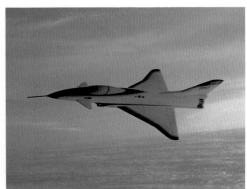

As with the Grumman X-29, the principal **raison d'être** for the X-31 is to investigate and develop methods for achieving a high degree of maneuverability at high speed. The project dates back to 1981, when Rockwell International in California approached Messerschmitt-Bolkow-Blohm (MBB) in Germany, which at that time was working on preliminary designs for the European Fighter Aircraft (EFA). Rockwell had in mind a system for post-stall maneuvering at very low speeds through the use of canards and thrust vectoring. MBB liked the concept, but it was too late to include it in its EFA proposal.

Two years later Rockwell approached the US Defense Advanced Research Projects Agency with a technology proposal it called 'Super-

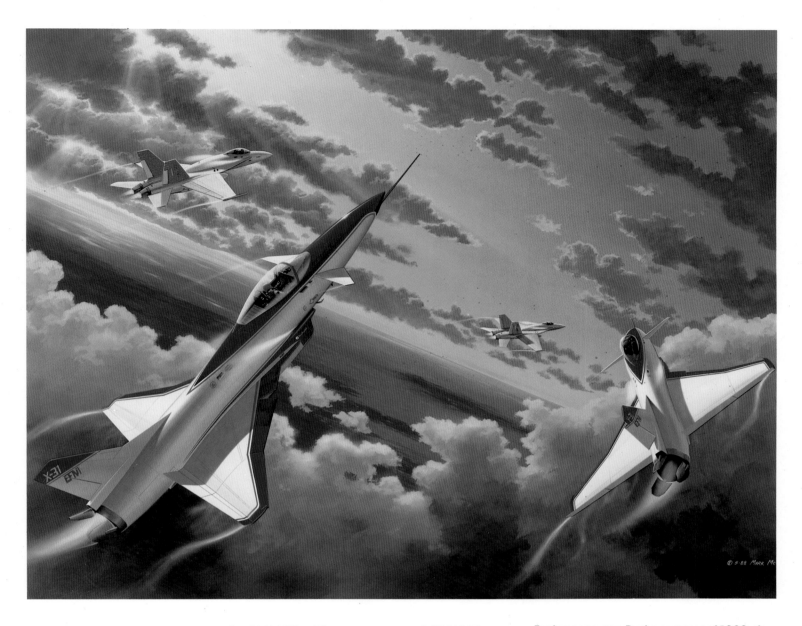

normal Kinetic Enhancement' (SNAKE). The essence of SNAKE was vectored engine thrust that was coordinated with aircraft control surfaces. SNAKE eventually evolved into Enhanced Fighter Maneuverability (EFM), which meant a regrettable loss of an acronym that perfectly described the way Rockwell's system would choreograph a flight.

In June 1986, the United States and West Germany formalized an agreement to jointly sponsor development of a demonstration aircraft based on the EFM technology that Rockwell and MBB had already been cooperating on for five years. The first of two X-31 aircraft was completed and flown at Rockwell's Palmdale, California test facility in 1990, and subsequently under the auspices of the US Navy at their test center at Patuxent River, Maryland.

The types of 'supermaneuver' of which the X-31 is capable are perhaps the ultimate in high performance fighter agility because of the g-force strain that such sudden and spectacular turns could potentially place upon the pilot. The EFM technology may well become standard equipment in the fighters of the twenty- first century, but to progress beyond this state-of-the-art will require advances not only in maneuvering technology but pilot survivability technology as well.

Facing page, top: **By the summer of 1989, the structure of the first X-31 prototype was largely complete at Rockwell's Palmdale, California facility.** *Facing page, bottom:* **A view of the X-31 banking for home just after dusk.** *Above:* **A 1988 painting by Mark McCandlish depicting a pair of X-31s deftly outturning McDonnell Douglas FA-18 Hornets in a mock dogfight over a curiously sepia landscape.**

THE NORTHROP B-2 STEALTH BOMBER
United States

Below: **A special musical piece, the *Stealth Fanfare*, was written for the 22 November 1988 rollout of the first Northrop B-2 strategic bomber. The music was traditional, but the airplane was like nothing anyone had ever seen.** *Right:* **The B-2 high in the stratosphere. Though it is pictured here at high altitude, the B-2 is optimized for low-altitude penetration missions.**

From the time she was first mentioned in public during the 1980 presidential campaign, she had a mystique that went far beyond any facts that we knew about her. If it hadn't been for the fact that President Jimmy Carter desperately needed a weapons system to hang his hat on, she might have remained secret for another decade. Carter was running an uphill election battle against Ronald Reagan, who promised to rebuild America's once-proud military might. Carter knew that the Air Force was secretly developing a revolutionary type of strategic bomber that employed a basket of technologies known as 'stealth' that would make it virtually invisible to enemy radar. In August 1988 he decided to let Defense Secretary Harold Brown leak just enough information about this 'stealth bomber' to make him appear to the public as one who quietly and secretly 'cared' about defense. Carter's ploy failed to get him elected, but it gave aviation enthusiasts and Soviet spies their first tantalizing inkling of the aircraft that would be '**the** mystery plane of the decade.'

The Reagan Administration brought down the veil of secrecy upon the 'stealth bomber' project, and little more was known for years. By 1985 it was learned that the prime contractor for the mystery ship was Northrop,

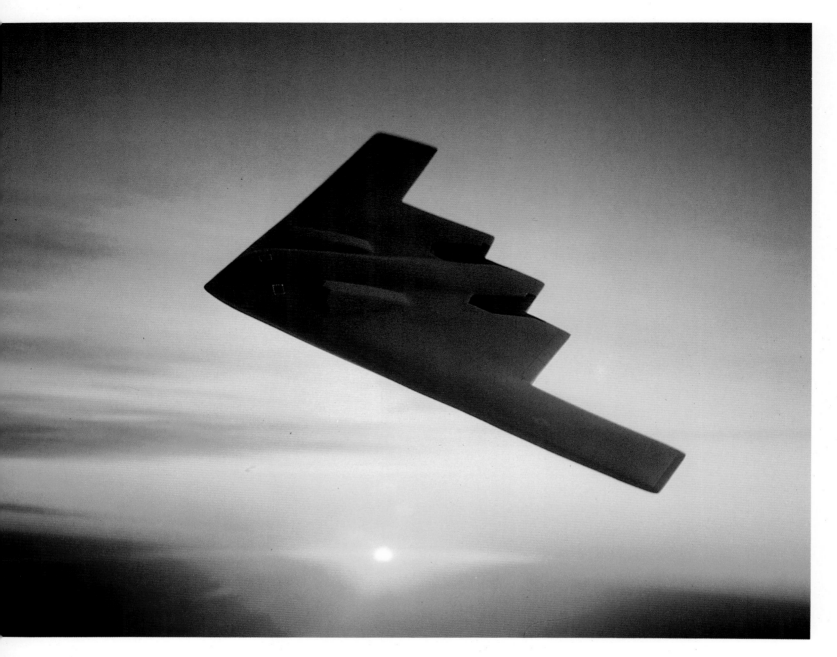

Above: **The startling silhouette of the Northrop B-2 is rendered on radar as a speck no larger than the radar signature of a western tanager.**

and this in turn led to speculation that the new airplane would have a 'flying wing' configuration because Northrop's only other heavy bombers had been the YB-35 and YB-49 Flying Wings of the early 1950s.

The B-2 rollout, on 22 November 1988, was the most heavily restricted **public** rollout in history. Indeed, there was a public rollout only because the Air Force decided that it would be impossible to flight test so large an aircraft in total secrecy. Only 500 guests were on hand, and armed guards outnumbered reporters by a ratio of four to one.

The first flight of the strange new airplane began at 6:37 am on 17 July with Northrop B-2 chief test pilot Bruce Hinds and Air Force Colonel Richard Couch in the cockpit. Much to the chagrin of Congressional critics, the flight went smoothly and the big bat touched down lightly at Edwards AFB at 8:29 am. The B-2 differs from the earlier YB-35 and YB-49 in that it has no vertical tail surfaces. Extremely sophisticated, quadruple-redundant, fly-by-wire digital electronic controls had eliminated the need for conventional rudders, as well as serving to solve the stability problem that was the Achilles heel of the YB-35 and YB-49.

Primary flight control consisted of three elevon surfaces on each wing and a rudder/spoiler at each wingtip. The outboard trailing edge had the drag rudder and the next inboard trailing edge surface had two more elevons. This system ingeniously eliminated the need for vertical tail surfaces and made it possible for the B-2 to make turns without a thrust-vectoring system, which some analysts had predicted that the long secret ship would use.

The most unique and important feature of the B-2—indeed its entire purpose for being—is its stealth technology. Stealth is, in fact, a whole basket of technologies designed to make the airplane virtually invisible to radar. These include contours and surfaces that absorb, rather than reflect, radar waves, thus giving the B-2 the radar signature more characteristic of a bird than a B-52.

It is ironic that William Cameron Menzies chose to picture flying wings in **Things to Come**. As it turned out, they, and the bizarre B-2, are in fact the **shape** of things to come, the shape of at least one important aspect of aviation technology in the twenty-first century.

Above: **With landing gear down in the approach position, the B-2 runs through its paces on its 17 July 1989 maiden flight. After takeoff** *(overleaf),* **the aircraft climbed to 10,000 feet, where functional checks of the basic subsystems were performed.**

Above: Hermes can spend up to 12 days in space before re-entry into the Earth's atmosphere, compared to a 30-day maximum duration for America's Rockwell Space Shuttle Orbiter. *At right:* After being launched by the Ariane 5, Hermes heads for the vast, dark reaches of space and a rendezvous with the space station *Columbus*.

THE HERMES SPACEPLANE
France

After 35 years of the Soviet Union and the United States having a monopoly on spacecraft capable of carrying human beings, France will be the first of several nations to develop an independent means of sending humans into space. After several years of preliminary studies, Philippe Couillard of France's National Center for Space Studies (CNES) announced in October 1985 that France's two largest aircraft builders, Dassault Breguet and Aerospatiale, had been selected to collaborate on the development of the Hermes spaceplane. Dassault Breguet would be responsible for the aerodynamics, airframe, flight testing and re-entry trajectory. Aerospatiale would plan the cockpit, avionics, power system and orbital operations. Approximately half of the total subsystems would be drawn from other European countries, such as Austria, Belgium, Denmark, Italy, the Netherlands, Sweden and Switzerland, which were partners with France in the European Space Agency (ESA). West Germany did not join the Hermes project initially because of prior commitments to its own Sanger spaceplane project.

With a length of 52 feet and a wingspan of 33 feet, the two-man Hermes spaceplane is less than half the size of the American Space Shuttle or Soviet Kosmolyet orbiters, but it is very close in size and configuration to the American Boeing X-20 spaceplane, which was built but never flown in the 1960s.

At left: **The HOPE is virtually a twin of the Hermes, with dimensions and shape almost identical. Like the Hermes, the HOPE is launched by a rocket with two strap-on boosters, a configuration borrowed from the American Martin Marietta Titan 3, which was first flown in the 1970s. Though both Hermes and HOPE can trace their roots back to the Boeing X-20, neither one has specific military applications.** *Above:* **An artist's rendering of the HOPE returning to Earth.**

A full-scale mockup of Hermes was unveiled at the Paris Air Show in June 1987, and it is expected to be in full operation by the turn of the century. It will be capable of commuting to both American and Soviet space stations and of flying independent missions to launch satellites from its payload bay. The Hermes vehicle is prototypical of a type of small spaceplane, which was predicted to come into service as early as the 1960s, but which will be part of routine space operations in the twenty-first century.

THE H-2 ORBITING PLANE
Japan

Like the Hermes spaceplane being developed in France, Japan's H-2 Orbiting Plane (HOPE) is a small, two-person spaceplane based on the Boeing X-20 of the 1960s, and is being designed for service prior to the turn of the century.

Engineered and built by Mitsubishi, the HOPE was first seen in preliminary form in March 1987, and a full-scale mockup was displayed at the 1989 Paris Air Show.

HOPE will be placed into orbit from the Japanese National Space Development Agency's (NASDA) Space Center at Tanegashima using an H-2 heavy lift booster rocket.

THE SANGER/HORUS SPACEPLANE
West Germany

At top: Sanger, a reusable two-stage aerospace plane for passengers and cargo transport, will be able to reach all Low Earth Orbits (LEO) from European airports.
Above: Similar to the Sanger project is Aerospatiale's AGV—Avion à Grande Vitesse. Unlike Sanger, however, the AGV is a *commercial* hypersonic transport. In the twenty-first century, the trip from San Francisco to Paris aboard the AGV—at Mach 5—will be over in the blink of an eye.
Opposite: Although this artist's rendering of the Sanger project has placed the spaceplane far above the Earth, only the smaller, second stage of Sanger will explore deep space.

During World War II, Dr Eugen Sanger (1903-1964) in Germany designed a horizontally launched, two-stage orbital spaceplane that he envisioned as being used as a bomber to hit targets in the United States or anywhere in the world. Sanger's revolutionary craft was never produced, but it did inspire a great many spaceplane design efforts in the 1950s, which culminated in the Boeing X-20 in the 1960s.

In the 1980s the German government decided to undertake development of a spaceplane based on Sanger's original concept. The project would be sponsored by the German Ministry for Research and Technology (BMFT) and the German Aerospace Research Agency (DLR), with participation by other members of the European Space Agency (ESA) as well. Unveiled in August 1986, the Sanger vehicle is seen by the Germans as a successor to the French Hermes spaceplane in the context of ESA-supported manned space flight.

The principal contractors for the project will be Messerschmitt-Bolkow-Blohm (MBB) for aerodynamics, guidance and navigation and Dornier for materials and structures. The engines will be constructed by Motoren & Turbinen Union (MTU).

As exhibited at the Paris Air Show in June 1989, the Sanger would be a horizontally-launched, completely reusable craft consisting of two stages, each of which would be an aerodynamic spaceplane. The larger of these, the first stage, would be 275 feet long, with a gross weight of 700,000 pounds, making it the same size as the largest jetliners. The second stage would consist of either the manned Hypersonic Orbital Upper Stage (HORUS) or the unmanned Cargo Upper Stage (CARGUS). The huge SCRAMJET (Supersonic Combustion Ramjet) powered first stage would carry the second stage to Mach 6.8 and an altitude of 19 miles, then released to fly into space under its own rocket propulsion. Both HORUS and CARGUS would be over 100 feet long and, as such, would be in the same size and weight class as the American Space Shuttle and Soviet Kosmolyet orbiters, although plans are under consideration to scale them down because the payload capacity is not needed.

The Sanger project is similar to the American X-30 and French **Avion à Grande Vitesse** (AGV) single-stage-to-orbit aircraft, insofar as all are designed for horizontal take-offs and are capable of carrying payloads roughly equal to those now carried by the Soviet and American shuttle systems.

It is indeed a fitting tribute to the man who conceived winged, horizontal take-off spacecraft in the mid-twentieth century that one such vehicle bearing his name will take wing in the twenty-first century.

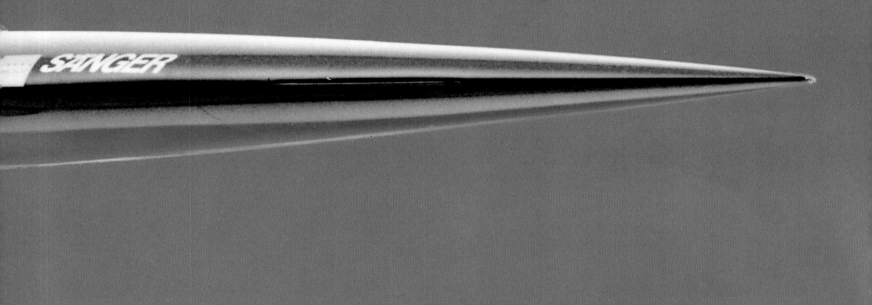

Above: The Sanger, cruising toward the ozone layer at Mach 5. Between Mach 6 and 7, the second stage—seen here riding piggy-back—will separate and fly into space under its own power. Their missions completed, both stages will return to the starting point.

INDEX

Opposite: **A US Air Force spaceplane returns to Earth from an orbital mission. Reusable spacecraft are an important part of the Air Force's desire to maintain a routine presence in space.** *Gatefold (outside):* **Lockheed F-22 fighters scamper among the clouds.** *Gatefold (inside):* **A US twenty-first century Navy fighter based on the Grumman X-29 research aircraft.**